all thumbs

all thumbs

cartoons by W Miller

with an introduction by Whitney Balliett

The Bobbs-Merrill Company, Inc.

A Subsidiary of Howard W. Sams and Co., Inc., Publishers

Indianapolis • Kansas City • New York

The cartoons appearing in this volume are reproduced
through the courtesy of *The New Yorker* magazine
and of *Punch* magazine, London, England.

introduction

Too often, lamentation is simply self-pity decked out as pity. One should read "Oh, my, the good old days are gone" as "Oh, Lord, I am forty and half my days are done." (Resurrecting the good old days, with their forgotten evils, would cause universal apoplexy.) One of the most fashionable laments bewails the passing of those emperors of humor the comic writers. Thurber, Benchley, Lardner, Parker, and Gibbs are gone, the cry goes. E. B. White is silent and Perelman is pre-emeritus. But this void has been filled; indeed, it runneth over. American writing is in one of its periodic retooling phases and those who might have been comic writers have turned to readier means of expression. They are stand-up comedians. They write or appear in funny radio and television commercials. They pose as politicians or jazz musicians or painters or hippies or "chance" composers. They draw cartoons. Perhaps the most dependable and prolific and comic of these funny men are the cartoonists. There are even two concurrent generations of them. The older is astonishingly resilient and includes Peter Arno, George Price, Steinberg, Alan Dunn, Charles Addams, and William Steig. The younger emerged barely a decade ago, but it already numbers Frank Modell, James Stevenson, Charles Saxon, Lee Lorenz, Donald Reilly, and Warren Miller. Needless to say, *The New Yorker* has been their forum and champion and, in most cases, discoverer.

Warren Miller is, I think, the most original and adventuresome of this new generation. (He signs his work W Miller and is not to be confused with the late novelist of the same name. Nor is he to be confused with a well-known skier of the same name, an Off-Off Broadway actor and playwright of the same name, or a New York typewriter service of the same name. *The* Warren Miller occasionally signs his letters "Warren Miller #5.") He joined *The New Yorker* just six years ago, but he has already turned out an extraordinary number of classic cartoons. He is, for one thing, a master of surprise. His ideas almost invariably go one ingenious step beyond what one expects. Consider the drawings dealing with those two treacherous times, late night and early morning. A drunk returns to his New York apartment building only to be told by his doorman that, doesn't he remember, he has moved to the suburbs. Another drunk, greeted by his wife at the door, finds himself encased in a giant empty bottle. A man answers his door bell and, confronted by a hideous devil, says, "Sorry, you have the wrong apartment, I'm on the wagon." A man pulls up his window shade one morning and discovers that the view is upside down. A man presses the button on his can of shaving cream and is jetted toward the ceiling on a stream of soap. But Miller's drawings are surprising, too. Unlike most cartoonists, he is not dominated by his style. His ideas are not propped up by his draftsmanship. Instead, his drawings *are* his ideas. Aristocratic types are done with spare lines and discreet backgrounds. Bums are heavily drawn and blurred. Crowd scenes are jostling and beautifully detailed. Cavemen are cavemen. His animals rival Audubon's. (Audubon depended on freshly killed animals for his models, but Miller's animal masterpiece in this collection is a giant dragon.) Most cartoonists mine the struggle between man and his environment, and Miller is no exception. But his best work is marked by a supreme and giddy sense of the ridiculous. A bird in a zoo asks another bird, "I'm a Wilson's snipe. What are you?" A Chinese stands on a crowd-encircled platform where a huge gong is about to be struck, and says to the crowd, "At the sound of the gong, everybody please say 'Goodbye Early Han Dynasty—Hello Later.'" (Almost all the cartoons in *All Thumbs* appeared in *The New Yorker,* but this marvel somehow ended up in *Punch.*) A night watchman, carrying a lantern, reels drunkenly up a dark village street and shouts, "It's one o'clock and I know something you don't know."

Miller is an oblique work of art himself. He is tall and round-faced and he looks twenty instead of thirty. He dresses like a rummage sale and he has a deep unintelligible voice. Like all first-class humorists, he is not interviewable:

Interviewer: Did you learn anything in the year you spent at art school in Chicago?

Miller: Ah . . . I don't know. We're still trying to figure that out.

Interviewer: Who was or who were your chief models?

Miller: Louis Armstrong.

Interviewer: What are your working habits?

Miller: What! Describe what you mean, please.

Interviewer: How did you happen to join *The New Yorker?*

Miller: I sent them a whole bunch of rough drawings which they kept a year. So I wrote them a letter. I don't remember what it said but they wrote back and invited me to New York for a talk. I went and they hired me.

He is a first-rate jazz trumpeter whose legato, detached style resembles that of the late, great Frankie Newton. He is that marvelous rarity—a genuinely shy man. (When he plays trumpet, he starts the evening somewhere near the band. An hour or two later, he will have edged into a far corner and on a couple of occasions he ended up playing by himself in an adjoining room.) He is a grateful gentle man who, while taking a summer stroll a couple of years ago, gingerly carried his two-month-old daughter in front of him on stiff outstretched arms, as if she were a platter of turkey. He is an excellent painter who has done the only comic semi-abstract still life of a bowl of flowers that I have ever seen. Above all, he is a funny man who is gracious enough to share his gifts.

Whitney Balliett
Glen Head, New York

"You really expect me to believe that you're a prince?"

"Have you never heard the old proverb 'An Albanian who eats with chopsticks bears watching'?"

"You're probably wondering why we asked you here today."

"Her Ladyship isn't in at the moment. She's out on the moors and fens."

*"It happens to be way after eleven,
and there are people trying to get some shut-eye around here!"*

"The earth is flat. Pass it on."

*"I hear the big change uptown
is from straight-up Martinis to Martinis on the rocks."*

"I'll bet that old guy has never blown his cool."

"I don't know how you feel, but I hate these company outings."

"I don't know anything about art, but I know what's 'in.'"

"Good afternoon, sir, we're taking a public-opinion poll on Vietnam. There are a few questions . . ."

"Could you possibly hold on a minute, please? I'll be right back."

"I said, 'I don't understand a word you're saying. Would you mind turning off the motor?'"

".K., pencil-pusher, fire away."

"Watch this!"

"Of course I love you,
but I'm running out of air."

"A-A-A-H! I've never felt so mortified!"

*"Hey, where are you trotting off to? I didn't slay
this thing just for my health, you know!"*

"May I congratulate you, sir, on your keen sense of history?"

"You heard the little lady, Mac. Act picturesque!"

"I know what I am, but I can't pronounce it."

"Everybody is getting flabby these days."

"It's a great act, but I miss the old style excitement."

"What do you mean, 'What does it _mean?_'"

"That was a stupid, childish, idiotic thing to say!"

"But you don't understand! I haven't even been to Europe yet!"

"Stop calling me Goldfinger!"

"For God's sake, just __boil__ it and __pour__ it!"

"Hey, Charlie! Look what I found at The Cloisters!"

"If you would rather do something else, son, say so. There's no law that says you <u>must</u> follow in your father's footsteps."

"Sister Theresa, who <u>was</u> St. Regis?"

"It's one o'clock and I know something you don't know."

"I'm going all the way to the bottom and let them think I'm extinct."

"Sam, you promised! 'For better or for worse!'"

"Don't you see, Roland, being a knight in shining armor isn't enough. All the fellows I know are knights in shining armor."

"*Maybe what you're trying to say, dear, just can't be said in that medium.*"

"*What gets me is that damn more-arcane-than-thou attitude of his.*"

"Our son marches to a distant drum."

"Have a bite of this, man, and get with it."

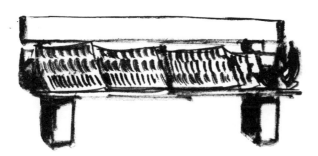

W. Miller

"So I don't understand you! That's what _you_ think!"

"You're in luck. I've got through to them both. Who do you want to talk to first, Mencken or Fitzgerald?"

"Hey! That's our last son!"

"I just got a B.A. at Bennington, and now I'm going to get __you__!"

"Advertise! Advertise! That's always been your answer to everything."

*"Buddy, you've called Vivaldi
the Dixieland of the classics for the last time!"*

"Please, lady, you're making it very difficult!"

"Where's the action?"

"Oh, knock it off! It's only cream of asparagus."

"My goodness, isn't this a pleasant planet!"

"You lily-livered safety buffs make me sick!"

"Dolores left me. I'm feeling bad,
Because my dad won't let me
Have a car, have a car, have a car!"

"Help! I'm being held prisoner!"

"For he's a jolly good fellow, for he's a jolly good fellow . . ."

"I have to go now, guys. It's time for Little League."

"Believe me, mister, I'm not really mean. It's just that I'm a firm believer in the theory of over-rob."

"Face it, baby. You don't know the warp from the woof."

"Please excuse me for a moment.
I just have to run up the clock."

"Face it, Toots, the old simpatico between us is kaputt!"

"You think you're so damn Cordon Bleu!"

"What I mean is, Leonardo, aren't you spreading yourself too thin?"

"Can anybody here <u>read</u>?"

"No, no, Mr. Fitzhugh! You moved to New Canaan. Remember?"

"Educational TV is for people who are unable to cope with real TV."

"Watch out, here it comes again!
'Existence is neither good nor evil. It simply is.'"

"You have the wrong apartment. I'm on the wagon!"

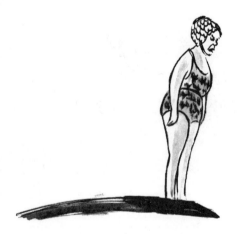

"Young lady, are you a member of this club?"

"No, no, Sugarplum. Only at the exact-change booths."

"Must you quote Mao Tse-tung at the breakfast table?"

"They'll never convince me there's no life on Mars!"

*"Good Lord! How early
do you have to be around here?"*

"Kicks! Kicks! All young people think about nowadays is kicks!"

"Get a shovel! We're the Boone Valley Ski Club!"

"Gee! We sure play a lot of swell teams!"

"I'm warning you two! Heads up and scintillate, or out you go!"

"*Pierre Augustin Caron du Beaumarchais!*"

"The bittersweet beauty of autumn means more to me than it does to others, perhaps. My species is only annual."

"I'll grant you his work has a certain naive immediacy."

"That's what comes of attaining satori too early in life."

"My goodness! It sure is offbeat!"

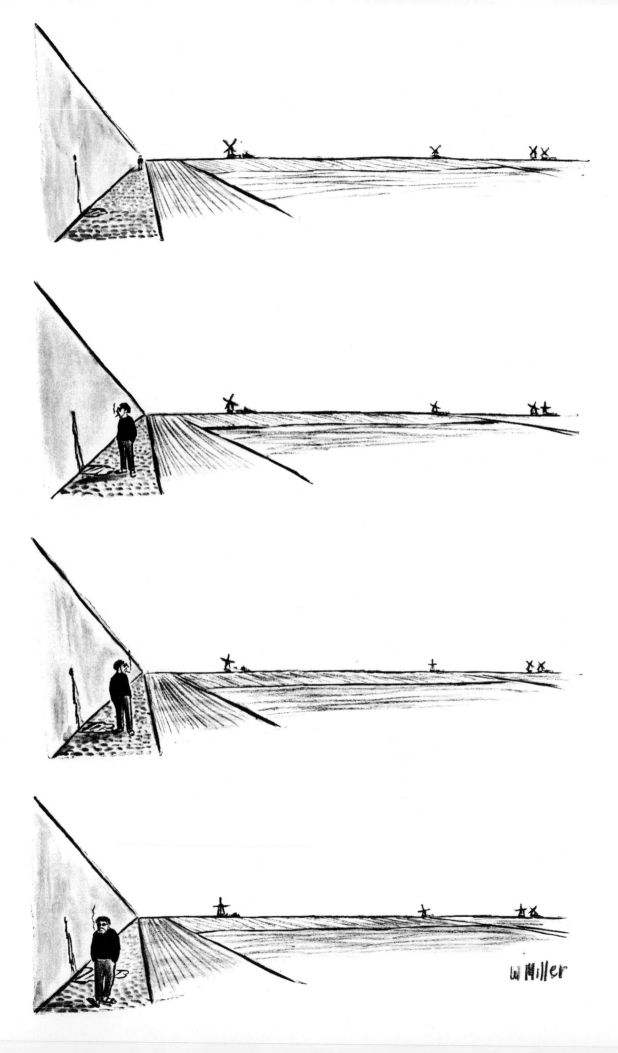

w Miller

"Why, it's Wally Bates! Have you forgotten that oath
we kids all took back in Buffalo, Wally?"

"He went down singing."

"…Data…Data…Data…Data…Data…Data…Data…Data…"

"We're supposed to watch you stroll by. You're not supposed
to stand and stare at us."

"Picasso! Another sacred cow!"

*"We're mighty fortunate, living, as we do, on an island where the sand is like
a golden carpet spread at our feet, the water is like some sparkling wine, and
the sun perpetually invites us to bask and revel in its healthgiving rays."*

*"One day last October, he said, 'I must go where the wild goose goes,'
and I haven't seen him since."*

*"At the sound of the gong, everybody please say
'Goodbye Early Han Dynasty—Hello Later!'"*

"Don't just glower at him, Daughter. Bat him over the head!"

"Just for that, __nobody__ gets my vote!"

*"I see you doing a rain dance. I see a hot-air mass.
Wait! I see a cold front moving in . . ."*

"Excuse me, but I've never hurled anything at an embassy before.
Is there a special technique?"

"Oooo, a whole peanut! . . . Thank you!"

"Edoardo, you tell them! Who discovered this place—them or us?"

"All I know is she never hangs around with the fun crowd."

WMiller

"I guess we can start phasing out the bow and arrow now."

"Money's tight, and so am I!"

"I guess I've been worrying about the Bomb."

"Well, I guess that's out as a sales gimmick."

"Buzz off, Ralphie!"

"Goodness! It is a pleasant vista!"

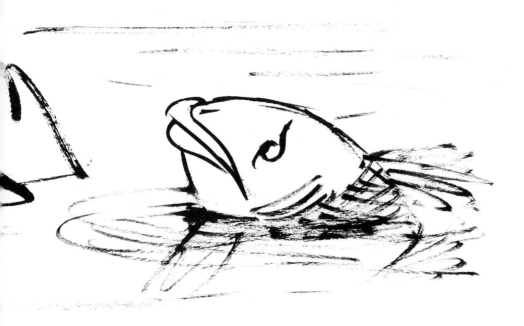

W Miller

"Whoops! The old clock on the wall says it's time for you
to pack up your troubles and shove along."

"You're home now. Stop comparing it with the Hasty Pudding Show."

"I'm a Wilson's snipe. What are you?"

"*The trouble with you is, you let your heart rule your head!*"

"Say 'Cheese.'"

"Hey! Where do you think you're going?"

"Cheese."

*"Boy, that guy sure knows what to say to make
you feel persona non grata!"*

"That's life."

"*This is a fine hour to come squeaking and creaking and clanking home.*"

TO THE
RAT RACE